SCHOLASTIC

Do The Math ™

Created by
Marilyn Burns

Fractions Ⓒ

Addition and Subtraction

....

WorkSpace

Copyright © 2008 by Scholastic Inc.

All rights reserved.   Published by Scholastic Inc.   Printed in the U.S.A.

ISBN-13: 978-0-545-02270-5
ISBN-10: 0-545-02270-3

SCHOLASTIC, DO THE MATH, and associated logos and designs are trademarks and/or registered trademarks of Scholastic Inc.

1   2   3   4   5   6   7   8   9   10   40   16   15   14   13   12   11   10   09   08   07

Add Fractions

1

$$\frac{3}{12} + \frac{3}{12} = \frac{6}{12} = \underline{\quad}$$

Write the answer.

2

$$\frac{3}{12} + \frac{3}{12} = \frac{6}{12} = \underline{\quad}$$

If possible, make an equivalent train using the fewest pieces.

3

$$\frac{3}{12} + \frac{3}{12} = \frac{6}{12} = \frac{1}{2}$$

Write the answer.

① $\frac{5}{12} + \frac{3}{12} = \underline{\quad} = \underline{\quad}$

② $\frac{1}{8} + \frac{3}{8} = \underline{\quad} = \underline{\quad}$

③ $\frac{5}{3} + \frac{2}{3} = \underline{\quad} = \underline{\quad}$

④ $\frac{3}{4} + \frac{2}{4} = \underline{\quad} = \underline{\quad}$

⑤ $\frac{5}{6} + \frac{3}{6} = \underline{\quad} = \underline{\quad}$

2 Lesson 1   **Home Note:** Your child uses fraction pieces to add fractions with like denominators.

Subtract Fractions

DIRECTIONS

1

$$\frac{7}{12} - \frac{3}{12} = \underline{\quad} = \underline{\quad}$$

$\frac{1}{12}\ \frac{1}{12}\ \frac{1}{12}\ \frac{1}{12}\ \frac{1}{12}\ \frac{1}{12}\ \frac{1}{12}$

Use fraction pieces
to make a train.

2

$\frac{1}{12}\ \frac{1}{12}\ \frac{1}{12}\ \frac{1}{12}$

$\frac{1}{3}$

Take away fraction pieces.
If possible, make an equivalent
train with fewer pieces.

3

$$\frac{7}{12} - \frac{3}{12} = \frac{4}{12} = \frac{1}{3}$$

Write the answer.

① $\dfrac{7}{8} - \dfrac{3}{8} = \underline{\quad} = \underline{\quad}$

② $1\dfrac{2}{4} - \dfrac{3}{4} = \underline{\quad} = \underline{\quad}$

③ $\dfrac{9}{12} - \dfrac{5}{12} = \underline{\quad} = \underline{\quad}$

④ $1\dfrac{2}{6} - \dfrac{5}{6} = \underline{\quad} = \underline{\quad}$

⑤ $\dfrac{15}{16} - \dfrac{9}{16} = \underline{\quad} = \underline{\quad}$

Home Note: Your child uses fraction pieces to subtract fractions with like denominators.

Add and Subtract Fractions and Mixed Numbers

DIRECTIONS

1

$$\frac{3}{4} + \frac{3}{8} = \boxed{>1}$$

Make an estimate.

2

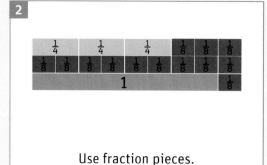

Use fraction pieces.

3

$$\frac{3}{4} + \frac{3}{8} =$$

$$\frac{6}{8} + \frac{3}{8} = \frac{9}{8} = 1\frac{1}{8}$$

>1

Rewrite the problem. Write the answer in lowest terms, or simplest form. Compare to estimate.

① $1\frac{1}{4} - \frac{3}{8} =$

② $\frac{3}{4} + \frac{5}{8} =$

③ $1\frac{1}{4} + \frac{1}{2} =$

④ $\frac{1}{3} + 1\frac{5}{6} =$

⑤ $\frac{5}{16} - \frac{1}{8} =$

Home Note: Your child uses fraction pieces to add and subtract fractions and mixed numbers.

Equivalent Fractions

DIRECTIONS

➤ Copy pairs of equivalent fractions from the class chart.

➤ Write more pairs of equivalent fractions as you continue the lessons.

$\frac{3}{4} = \frac{6}{8}$	

Home Note: Your child uses multiplication to write pairs of equivalent fractions.

Solve Addition and Subtraction Problems

DIRECTIONS

1

$$\frac{1}{4} + \frac{5}{8} =$$

Make an estimate.

2

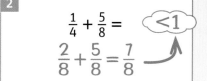

$$\frac{1}{4} + \frac{5}{8} = \quad <1$$

$$\frac{2}{8} + \frac{5}{8} = \frac{7}{8}$$

Rewrite the problem.
Write the answer in lowest
terms. Compare to estimate.

3

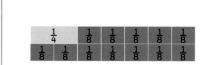

Use fraction pieces
to check your answer.

① $\frac{5}{6} - \frac{3}{12} =$

② $1\frac{1}{12} + \frac{1}{6} =$

③ $\frac{3}{8} + \frac{4}{16} =$

④ $1\frac{3}{8} - \frac{1}{2} =$

Home Note: Your child uses equivalent fractions to add
and subtract fractions and mixed numbers.

Show What You Know

DIRECTIONS

➤ Make an estimate.
➤ Rewrite the problem.
   Write the answer in lowest terms.
➤ Compare to estimate.

① $\frac{3}{8} + \frac{3}{16} =$

② $1\frac{1}{6} + \frac{1}{2} =$

③ $\frac{7}{8} + \frac{1}{4} =$

④ $1\frac{7}{8} - \frac{3}{4} =$

Home Note: Your child uses equivalent fractions to add and subtract fractions and mixed numbers.

Show What You Know

⑤ $1\frac{1}{2} - \frac{1}{4} =$

⑥ $\frac{5}{6} + \frac{5}{12} =$

⑦ $1\frac{3}{8} - \frac{3}{4} =$

⑧ $\frac{7}{8} - \frac{3}{4} =$

Home Note: Your child writes equivalent fractions and solves addition and subtraction problems.

Fractions Equivalent to $\frac{1}{2}$

➤ Copy the equations showing fractions equivalent to $\frac{1}{2}$ from the class chart.

➤ Write more equations showing fractions equivalent to $\frac{1}{2}$.

$\frac{1}{2} = \frac{2}{4}$	
$\frac{1}{2} = \frac{3}{6}$	

Home Note: Your child writes fractions equivalent to $\frac{1}{2}$.

Add and Subtract with $\frac{1}{2}$

1

$\frac{1}{2} + \frac{2}{6} =$ <1

Make an estimate.

2

$\frac{1}{2} + \frac{2}{6} =$ <1

$\frac{3}{6} + \frac{2}{6} = \frac{5}{6}$

Rewrite the problem.
Write the answer in lowest terms.

3

$\frac{1}{2} + \frac{2}{6} =$ <1

$\frac{3}{6} + \frac{2}{6} = \frac{5}{6}$

Compare answer
to estimate.

① $\frac{1}{2} - \frac{5}{12} =$

② $\frac{5}{6} - \frac{1}{2} =$

③ $\frac{8}{10} - \frac{1}{2} =$

④ $\frac{10}{16} + \frac{1}{2} =$

⑤ $\frac{1}{2} + \frac{7}{8} =$

Home Note: Your child renames $\frac{1}{2}$ to get common denominators and then adds and subtracts fractions.

Fractions Equivalent to $\frac{1}{4}$

➤ Copy the equations showing fractions equivalent to $\frac{1}{4}$ from the class chart.

➤ Write more equations showing fractions equivalent to $\frac{1}{4}$.

$\frac{1}{4} = \frac{2}{8}$	

Home Note: Your child writes fractions equivalent to $\frac{1}{4}$.

Add and Subtract with $\frac{1}{4}$

1

$\frac{1}{4} + \frac{2}{16} =$

⟨<1⟩

Make an estimate.

2

$\frac{1}{4} + \frac{2}{16} =$

⟨<1⟩

$\frac{4}{16} + \frac{2}{16} = \frac{6}{16} = \frac{3}{8}$

Rewrite the problem. Write the answer in lowest terms.

3

$\frac{1}{4} + \frac{2}{16} =$

⟨<1⟩

$\frac{4}{16} + \frac{2}{16} = \frac{6}{16} = \frac{3}{8}$

Compare answer to estimate.

① $\frac{11}{16} - \frac{1}{4} =$

② $\frac{1}{4} + \frac{7}{8} =$

③ $\frac{1}{4} + \frac{5}{16} =$

④ $\frac{7}{12} + \frac{1}{4} =$

⑤ $\frac{7}{8} - \frac{1}{4} =$

⑥ $\frac{9}{12} + \frac{1}{4} =$

12 Lesson 9

Home Note: Your child renames $\frac{1}{4}$ to get common denominators and then adds and subtracts fractions.

Show What You Know

DIRECTIONS

➤ Make an estimate.

➤ Rewrite the problem.

➤ Write the answer in lowest terms.

➤ Compare your answer to your estimate.

① $\frac{1}{2} + \frac{2}{10} = \frac{2}{10}$

② $\frac{7}{8} - \frac{1}{2} =$

③ $\frac{1}{4} + \frac{11}{12} =$

④ $\frac{9}{12} - \frac{1}{4} =$

⑤ $\frac{5}{6} + \frac{1}{2} =$

Home Note: Your child renames $\frac{1}{2}$ and $\frac{1}{4}$ to get common denominators and then adds and subtracts fractions.

Lesson 10 **13**

Game Rules for Compute & Compare

What you need

- *Compute & Compare Cards A*
- *Compute & Compare Board 1*
- *WorkSpace* page 15

➤ **A team can't have more than two cards with the same number.**

➤ **A team can't make an improper fraction or a fraction equal to 1.**

1

Team A	Team B
2 2 1 4	1 4 1 8

Each team turns over four cards.

2

Team A	Team B

Each team places the cards on the board.

3

Team A
$$\frac{2}{4}+\frac{1}{2}=\boxed{1}$$

Team B
$$\frac{1}{4}+\frac{1}{8}=\frac{3}{8}$$

Add the fractions and write equations.
Circle the greater answer.

➤ **The winner is the team with the greater sum.**

Home Note: Your child practices adding and comparing fractions by playing a game.

Compute & Compare with Cards A

DIRECTIONS

1

$$\frac{\boxed{2}}{\boxed{4}} + \frac{\boxed{1}}{\boxed{2}}$$

$$\frac{2}{4} + \frac{1}{2} = 1$$

Record your fractions.
Add. Write an equation.

2

$$\frac{\boxed{1}}{\boxed{4}} + \frac{\boxed{1}}{\boxed{8}}$$

$$\frac{1}{4} + \frac{1}{8} = \frac{3}{8}$$

Record the other team's
fractions and equation.

3

$$\frac{2}{4} + \frac{1}{2} = \boxed{1} \qquad \frac{1}{4} + \frac{1}{8} = \frac{3}{8}$$

Circle the greater sum.

Game 1	Your Team	Other Team
	$\dfrac{\boxed{}}{\boxed{}} + \dfrac{\boxed{}}{\boxed{}}$ Equation:	$\dfrac{\boxed{}}{\boxed{}} + \dfrac{\boxed{}}{\boxed{}}$ Equation:
Game 2	Your Team	Other Team
	$\dfrac{\boxed{}}{\boxed{}} + \dfrac{\boxed{}}{\boxed{}}$ Equation:	$\dfrac{\boxed{}}{\boxed{}} + \dfrac{\boxed{}}{\boxed{}}$ Equation:

Home Note: Your child practices adding and comparing fractions by playing a game.

Compute & Compare with Cards A

DIRECTIONS

1

$$\frac{2}{4} + \frac{1}{2}$$

$$\frac{2}{4} + \frac{1}{2} = 1$$

Record your fractions.
Add. Write an equation.

2

$$\frac{1}{4} + \frac{1}{8}$$

$$\frac{1}{4} + \frac{1}{8} = \frac{3}{8}$$

Record the other team's
fractions and equation.

3

$$\frac{2}{4} + \frac{1}{2} = 1 \quad \frac{1}{4} + \frac{1}{8} = \boxed{\frac{3}{8}}$$

Circle the lesser sum.

Game 1	Your Team	Other Team
	$$\frac{\square}{\square} + \frac{\square}{\square}$$	$$\frac{\square}{\square} + \frac{\square}{\square}$$
	Equation:	Equation:
Game 2	**Your Team**	**Other Team**
	$$\frac{\square}{\square} + \frac{\square}{\square}$$	$$\frac{\square}{\square} + \frac{\square}{\square}$$
	Equation:	Equation:

 **Home Note:** Your child practices adding and comparing fractions by playing a game.

Game Rules for Compute & Compare with Three Addends

What you need

- *Compute & Compare* Cards A
- *Compute & Compare* Board 2
- *WorkSpace* page 18

➤ **A team can't have more than two cards with the same number.**

➤ **A team can't make an improper fraction or a fraction equal to 1.**

1   **Team A**

1	2	8	4	4	1

Each team turns over six cards.

2   **Team A**

$$\frac{4}{8} + \frac{1}{2} + \frac{1}{4}$$

Each team places the cards on the board.

3   **Team A**

$$\frac{4}{8} + \frac{1}{2} + \frac{1}{4} = 1\frac{1}{4}$$

Add the fractions and write an equation.

➤ **The winner is the team with the greater sum.**

Home Note: Your child practices adding and comparing fractions by playing a game.

Compute & Compare with Cards A

1

$$\frac{\boxed{1}}{\boxed{4}} + \frac{\boxed{2}}{\boxed{4}} + \frac{\boxed{1}}{\boxed{8}}$$

$$\frac{1}{4} + \frac{2}{4} + \frac{1}{8} = \frac{7}{8}$$

Record your fractions.
Add. Write an equation.

2

$$\frac{\boxed{2}}{\boxed{4}} + \frac{\boxed{4}}{\boxed{8}} + \frac{\boxed{1}}{\boxed{2}}$$

$$\frac{2}{4} + \frac{4}{8} + \frac{1}{2} = 1\frac{1}{2}$$

Record the other team's
fractions and equation.

3

$$\frac{1}{4} + \frac{2}{4} + \frac{1}{8} = \frac{7}{8}$$

$$\frac{2}{4} + \frac{4}{8} + \frac{1}{2} = \boxed{1\frac{1}{2}}$$

Circle the greater sum.

Game 1	Your Team	Other Team
	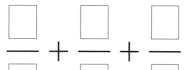	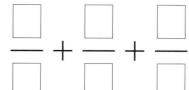
	Equation:	Equation:
Game 2	Your Team	Other Team
	$$\frac{\square}{\square} + \frac{\square}{\square} + \frac{\square}{\square}$$	$$\frac{\square}{\square} + \frac{\square}{\square} + \frac{\square}{\square}$$
	Equation:	Equation:

Home Note: Your child practices adding and comparing fractions by playing a game.

Compute & Compare with Cards A

1

$$\frac{\boxed{1}}{\boxed{4}} + \frac{\boxed{2}}{\boxed{4}} + \frac{\boxed{1}}{\boxed{8}}$$

$$\frac{1}{4} + \frac{2}{4} + \frac{1}{8} = \frac{7}{8}$$

Record your fractions.
Add. Write an equation.

2

$$\frac{\boxed{2}}{\boxed{4}} + \frac{\boxed{4}}{\boxed{8}} + \frac{\boxed{1}}{\boxed{2}}$$

$$\frac{2}{4} + \frac{4}{8} + \frac{1}{2} = 1\frac{1}{2}$$

Record the other team's
fractions and equation.

3

$$\frac{1}{4} + \frac{2}{4} + \frac{1}{8} = \frac{7}{8}$$

$$\frac{2}{4} + \frac{4}{8} + \frac{1}{2} = \boxed{1\frac{1}{2}}$$

Circle the greater sum.

Game 1	Your Team	Other Team
	$$\frac{\square}{\square} + \frac{\square}{\square} + \frac{\square}{\square}$$	$$\frac{\square}{\square} + \frac{\square}{\square} + \frac{\square}{\square}$$
	Equation:	Equation:
Game 2	Your Team	Other Team
	$$\frac{\square}{\square} + \frac{\square}{\square} + \frac{\square}{\square}$$	$$\frac{\square}{\square} + \frac{\square}{\square} + \frac{\square}{\square}$$
	Equation:	Equation:

Home Note: Your child practices adding and comparing fractions by playing a game.

Lesson 12

Compute & Compare with Cards A

DIRECTIONS

1

$$\frac{\boxed{1}}{\boxed{4}} + \frac{\boxed{2}}{\boxed{4}} + \frac{\boxed{1}}{\boxed{8}}$$

$$\frac{1}{4} + \frac{2}{4} + \frac{1}{8} = \frac{7}{8}$$

Record your fractions.
Add. Write an equation.

2

$$\frac{\boxed{2}}{\boxed{4}} + \frac{\boxed{4}}{\boxed{8}} + \frac{\boxed{1}}{\boxed{2}}$$

$$\frac{2}{4} + \frac{4}{8} + \frac{1}{2} = 1\frac{1}{2}$$

Record the other team's
fractions and equation.

3

$$\frac{1}{4} + \frac{2}{4} + \frac{1}{8} = \boxed{\frac{7}{8}}$$

$$\frac{2}{4} + \frac{4}{8} + \frac{1}{2} = 1\frac{1}{2}$$

Circle the lesser sum.

Game 1	Your Team	Other Team
	$\dfrac{\boxed{}}{\boxed{}} + \dfrac{\boxed{}}{\boxed{}} + \dfrac{\boxed{}}{\boxed{}}$	$\dfrac{\boxed{}}{\boxed{}} + \dfrac{\boxed{}}{\boxed{}} + \dfrac{\boxed{}}{\boxed{}}$
	Equation:	Equation:
Game 2	Your Team	Other Team
	$\dfrac{\boxed{}}{\boxed{}} + \dfrac{\boxed{}}{\boxed{}} + \dfrac{\boxed{}}{\boxed{}}$	$\dfrac{\boxed{}}{\boxed{}} + \dfrac{\boxed{}}{\boxed{}} + \dfrac{\boxed{}}{\boxed{}}$
	Equation:	Equation:

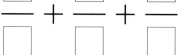 **Home Note:** Your child practices adding and comparing fractions by playing a game.

Compute & Compare with Cards A

1

$$\frac{1}{4} + \frac{2}{4} + \frac{1}{8}$$

$$\frac{1}{4} + \frac{2}{4} + \frac{1}{8} = \frac{7}{8}$$

Record your fractions.
Add. Write an equation.

2

$$\frac{2}{4} + \frac{4}{8} + \frac{1}{2}$$

$$\frac{2}{4} + \frac{4}{8} + \frac{1}{2} = 1\frac{1}{2}$$

Record the other team's
fractions and equation.

3

$$\frac{1}{4} + \frac{2}{4} + \frac{1}{8} = \boxed{\frac{7}{8}}$$

$$\frac{2}{4} + \frac{4}{8} + \frac{1}{2} = 1\frac{1}{2}$$

Circle the lesser sum.

Game 1	Your Team	Other Team
	$$\frac{\square}{\square} + \frac{\square}{\square} + \frac{\square}{\square}$$	$$\frac{\square}{\square} + \frac{\square}{\square} + \frac{\square}{\square}$$
	Equation:	Equation:
Game 2	**Your Team**	**Other Team**
	$$\frac{\square}{\square} + \frac{\square}{\square} + \frac{\square}{\square}$$	$$\frac{\square}{\square} + \frac{\square}{\square} + \frac{\square}{\square}$$
	Equation:	Equation:

Home Note: Your child practices adding and comparing fractions by playing a game.

Compute & Compare with Cards A

1

$$\frac{\boxed{1}}{\boxed{4}} + \frac{\boxed{2}}{\boxed{4}} + \frac{\boxed{1}}{\boxed{8}}$$

$$\frac{1}{4} + \frac{2}{4} + \frac{1}{8} = \frac{7}{8}$$

Record your fractions.
Add. Write an equation.

2

$$\frac{\boxed{2}}{\boxed{4}} + \frac{\boxed{4}}{\boxed{8}} + \frac{\boxed{1}}{\boxed{2}}$$

$$\frac{2}{4} + \frac{4}{8} + \frac{1}{2} = 1\frac{1}{2}$$

Record the other team's
fractions and equation.

3

$$\frac{1}{4} + \frac{2}{4} + \frac{1}{8} = \boxed{\frac{7}{8}}$$

$$\frac{2}{4} + \frac{4}{8} + \frac{1}{2} = 1\frac{1}{2}$$

Circle the lesser sum.

Game 1	Your Team	Other Team
	$\dfrac{\Box}{\Box} + \dfrac{\Box}{\Box} + \dfrac{\Box}{\Box}$	$\dfrac{\Box}{\Box} + \dfrac{\Box}{\Box} + \dfrac{\Box}{\Box}$
	Equation:	Equation:
Game 2	Your Team	Other Team
	$\dfrac{\Box}{\Box} + \dfrac{\Box}{\Box} + \dfrac{\Box}{\Box}$	$\dfrac{\Box}{\Box} + \dfrac{\Box}{\Box} + \dfrac{\Box}{\Box}$
	Equation:	Equation:

Home Note: Your child practices adding and comparing fractions by playing a game.

Equivalent Fractions Sequences

EQUIVALENT FRACTIONS SEQUENCES					
	$\dfrac{\times 2}{\times 2}$	$\dfrac{\times 3}{\times 3}$	$\dfrac{\times 4}{\times 4}$	$\dfrac{\times 5}{\times 5}$	$\dfrac{\times 6}{\times 6}$ $\cdots$
$\dfrac{1}{2},$					
$\dfrac{1}{3},$					
$\dfrac{1}{4},$					
$\dfrac{2}{3},$					
$\dfrac{3}{4},$					

Home Note: Your child writes sequences of equivalent fractions.

Compute & Compare with Cards A

1

$$\frac{\boxed{1}}{\boxed{4}} + \frac{\boxed{2}}{\boxed{4}} + \frac{\boxed{1}}{\boxed{8}}$$

$$\frac{1}{4} + \frac{2}{4} + \frac{1}{8} = \frac{7}{8}$$

Record your fractions. Add. Write an equation.

2

$$\frac{\boxed{2}}{\boxed{4}} + \frac{\boxed{4}}{\boxed{8}} + \frac{\boxed{1}}{\boxed{2}}$$

$$\frac{2}{4} + \frac{4}{8} + \frac{1}{2} = 1\frac{1}{2}$$

Record the other team's fractions and equation.

3

$$\frac{1}{4} + \frac{2}{4} + \frac{1}{8} = \frac{7}{8}$$

$$\frac{2}{4} + \frac{4}{8} + \frac{1}{2} = \boxed{1\frac{1}{2}}$$

Circle the greater sum.

Game 1	Your Team	Other Team
	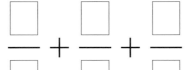	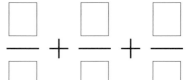
	Equation:	Equation:

Game 2	Your Team	Other Team
	$\frac{\Box}{\Box} + \frac{\Box}{\Box} + \frac{\Box}{\Box}$	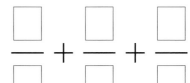
	Equation:	Equation:

Home Note: Your child practices adding and comparing fractions by playing a game.

Show What You Know

➤ Use the numbers to make fractions with the greatest sum possible.

➤ Write your equation with the answer in lowest terms.

① 1 4 8 8

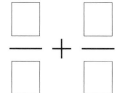

Equation:

② 2 1 1 4

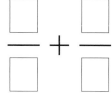

Equation:

③ 1 2 4 4 8 8

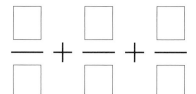

Equation:

④ 1 1 4 4 2 2

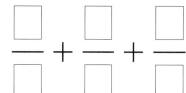

Equation:

Home Note: Your child practices adding and comparing fractions.

Compute & Compare with Cards A

DIRECTIONS

1

$$\frac{\boxed{1}}{\boxed{4}} + \frac{\boxed{2}}{\boxed{4}} + \frac{\boxed{1}}{\boxed{8}}$$

$$\frac{1}{4} + \frac{2}{4} + \frac{1}{8} = \frac{7}{8}$$

Record your fractions.
Add. Write an equation.

2

$$\frac{\boxed{2}}{\boxed{4}} + \frac{\boxed{4}}{\boxed{8}} + \frac{\boxed{1}}{\boxed{2}}$$

$$\frac{2}{4} + \frac{4}{8} + \frac{1}{2} = 1\frac{1}{2}$$

Record the other team's
fractions and equation.

3

$$\frac{1}{4} + \frac{2}{4} + \frac{1}{8} = \frac{7}{8}$$

$$\frac{2}{4} + \frac{4}{8} + \frac{1}{2} = \boxed{1\frac{1}{2}}$$

Circle the greater sum.

Game 1	Your Team	Other Team
	$$\frac{\square}{\square} + \frac{\square}{\square} + \frac{\square}{\square}$$	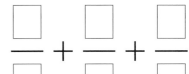
	Equation:	Equation:
Game 2	Your Team	Other Team
	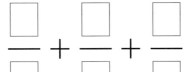	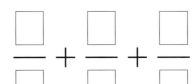
	Equation:	Equation:

Home Note: Your child practices adding and comparing fractions by playing a game.

Compute & Compare with Cards B

DIRECTIONS

1

$$\frac{2}{4} + \frac{1}{2}$$

$$\frac{2}{4} + \frac{1}{2} = 1$$

Record your fractions.
Add. Write an equation.

2

$$\frac{1}{4} + \frac{1}{8}$$

$$\frac{1}{4} + \frac{1}{8} = \frac{3}{8}$$

Record the other team's
fractions and equation.

3

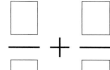

$$\frac{2}{4} + \frac{1}{2} = ①\qquad \frac{1}{4} + \frac{1}{8} = \frac{3}{8}$$

Circle the greater sum.

Game 1	Your Team	Other Team
	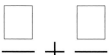 $\dfrac{\square}{\square} + \dfrac{\square}{\square}$	$\dfrac{\square}{\square} + \dfrac{\square}{\square}$
	Equation:	Equation:
Game 2	Your Team	Other Team
	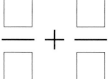 $\dfrac{\square}{\square} + \dfrac{\square}{\square}$	 $\dfrac{\square}{\square} + \dfrac{\square}{\square}$
	Equation:	Equation:

 Home Note: Your child practices adding and comparing fractions by playing a game.

Compute & Compare with Cards B

DIRECTIONS

1

$$\frac{\boxed{2}}{\boxed{4}} + \frac{\boxed{1}}{\boxed{2}}$$

$$\frac{2}{4} + \frac{1}{2} = 1$$

Record your fractions.
Add. Write an equation.

2

$$\frac{\boxed{1}}{\boxed{4}} + \frac{\boxed{1}}{\boxed{8}}$$

$$\frac{1}{4} + \frac{1}{8} = \frac{3}{8}$$

Record the other team's
fractions and equation.

3

$$\frac{2}{4} + \frac{1}{2} = ① \qquad \frac{1}{4} + \frac{1}{8} = \frac{3}{8}$$

Circle the greater sum.

Game 1	Your Team	Other Team
		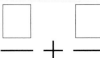
	Equation:	Equation:
Game 2	Your Team	Other Team
		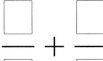
	Equation:	Equation:

Home Note: Your child practices adding and comparing fractions by playing a game.

Possible Addition Problems for 1, 3, 2, 6, 3, 4

DIRECTIONS

➤ Complete this page as your teacher directs.

Team 1

1 3 2 6 3 4

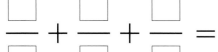

$$\frac{\square}{\square} + \frac{\square}{\square} + \frac{\square}{\square} =$$

$$\frac{\square}{\square} + \frac{\square}{\square} + \frac{\square}{\square} =$$

$$\frac{\square}{\square} + \frac{\square}{\square} + \frac{\square}{\square} =$$

$$\frac{\square}{\square} + \frac{\square}{\square} + \frac{\square}{\square} =$$

$$\frac{\square}{\square} + \frac{\square}{\square} + \frac{\square}{\square} =$$

Home Note: Your child practices adding and comparing fractions by playing a game.

Possible Addition Problems for 1, 6, 2, 4, 4, 3

➤ Complete this page as your teacher directs.

Team 2

1 6 2 4 4 3

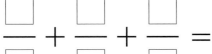

$$\frac{\square}{\square} + \frac{\square}{\square} + \frac{\square}{\square} =$$

$$\frac{\square}{\square} + \frac{\square}{\square} + \frac{\square}{\square} =$$

$$\frac{\square}{\square} + \frac{\square}{\square} + \frac{\square}{\square} =$$

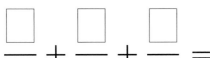

$$\frac{\square}{\square} + \frac{\square}{\square} + \frac{\square}{\square} =$$

$$\frac{\square}{\square} + \frac{\square}{\square} + \frac{\square}{\square} =$$

Home Note: Your child practices adding and comparing fractions.

Compute & Compare with Cards B

DIRECTIONS

1

$$\frac{1}{4} + \frac{2}{4} + \frac{1}{8}$$

$$\frac{1}{4} + \frac{2}{4} + \frac{1}{8} = \frac{7}{8}$$

Record your fractions.
Add. Write an equation.

2

$$\frac{2}{4} + \frac{4}{8} + \frac{1}{2}$$

$$\frac{2}{4} + \frac{4}{8} + \frac{1}{2} = 1\frac{1}{2}$$

Record the other team's
fractions and equation.

3

$$\frac{1}{4} + \frac{2}{4} + \frac{1}{8} = \frac{7}{8}$$

$$\frac{2}{4} + \frac{4}{8} + \frac{1}{2} = \boxed{1\frac{1}{2}}$$

Circle the greater sum.

Game 1	Your Team	Other Team
	$\dfrac{\square}{\square} + \dfrac{\square}{\square} + \dfrac{\square}{\square}$	$\dfrac{\square}{\square} + \dfrac{\square}{\square} + \dfrac{\square}{\square}$
	Equation:	Equation:
Game 2	Your Team	Other Team
	$\dfrac{\square}{\square} + \dfrac{\square}{\square} + \dfrac{\square}{\square}$	$\dfrac{\square}{\square} + \dfrac{\square}{\square} + \dfrac{\square}{\square}$
	Equation:	Equation:

Home Note: Your child practices adding and comparing fractions by playing a game.

Compute & Compare with Cards B

DIRECTIONS

1

$$\frac{\boxed{1}}{\boxed{4}} + \frac{\boxed{2}}{\boxed{4}} + \frac{\boxed{1}}{\boxed{8}}$$

$$\frac{1}{4} + \frac{2}{4} + \frac{1}{8} = \frac{7}{8}$$

Record your fractions.
Add. Write an equation.

2

$$\frac{\boxed{2}}{\boxed{4}} + \frac{\boxed{4}}{\boxed{8}} + \frac{\boxed{1}}{\boxed{2}}$$

$$\frac{2}{4} + \frac{4}{8} + \frac{1}{2} = 1\frac{1}{2}$$

Record the other team's
fractions and equation.

3

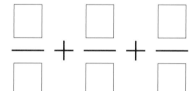

$$\frac{1}{4} + \frac{2}{4} + \frac{1}{8} = \frac{7}{8}$$

$$\frac{2}{4} + \frac{4}{8} + \frac{1}{2} = \boxed{1\frac{1}{2}}$$

Circle the greater sum.

Game 1	Your Team	Other Team
	$$\frac{\Box}{\Box} + \frac{\Box}{\Box} + \frac{\Box}{\Box}$$	$$\frac{\Box}{\Box} + \frac{\Box}{\Box} + \frac{\Box}{\Box}$$
	Equation:	Equation:
Game 2	Your Team	Other Team
	$$\frac{\Box}{\Box} + \frac{\Box}{\Box} + \frac{\Box}{\Box}$$	$$\frac{\Box}{\Box} + \frac{\Box}{\Box} + \frac{\Box}{\Box}$$
	Equation:	Equation:

Home Note: Your child practices adding and comparing fractions by playing a game.

Add and Subtract Fractions with Unlike Denominators

1

$\frac{1}{3} + \frac{1}{4} =$ >1

Make an estimate.

2

$\frac{1}{3}, \frac{2}{6}, \frac{3}{9}, \mathbf{\frac{4}{12}}, \frac{5}{15}, \frac{6}{18}, \cdots$

$\frac{1}{4}, \frac{2}{8}, \mathbf{\frac{3}{12}}, \cdots$

Write sequences of equivalent fractions.

3

$\frac{1}{3} + \frac{1}{4} =$ >1

$\frac{4}{12} + \frac{3}{12} = \frac{7}{12}$

Rewrite the problem.
Write the answer in lowest terms.
Compare answer and estimate.

① $\frac{2}{3} - \frac{1}{4} =$

② $1\frac{1}{6} + \frac{3}{4} =$

③ $1\frac{1}{4} - \frac{2}{3} =$

④ $\frac{5}{6} + \frac{1}{4} =$

Home Note: Your child uses sequences to get common denominators and then adds and subtracts fractions.

Add and Subtract Fractions with Unlike Denominators

DIRECTIONS

1

$$\frac{1}{3} + \frac{1}{4} = \boxed{>1}$$

Make an estimate.

2

$$\frac{1}{3}, \frac{2}{6}, \frac{3}{9}, \mathbf{\frac{4}{12}}, \frac{5}{15}, \frac{6}{18}, \cdots$$
$$\frac{1}{4}, \frac{2}{8}, \mathbf{\frac{3}{12}}, \cdots$$

Write sequences of equivalent fractions.

3

$$\frac{1}{3} + \frac{1}{4} = \qquad \boxed{>1}$$
$$\frac{4}{12} + \frac{3}{12} = \frac{7}{12}$$

Rewrite the problem.
Write the answer in lowest terms.
Compare answer and estimate.

① $\frac{2}{3} + \frac{1}{8} =$

② $\frac{1}{2} + \frac{3}{5} =$

③ $\frac{5}{6} - \frac{3}{8} =$

④ $1\frac{4}{5} - \frac{1}{2} =$

Home Note: Your child uses sequences to get common denominators and then adds and subtracts fractions.

Compute & Compare with Cards B

DIRECTIONS

1

$$\frac{1}{4} + \frac{2}{4} + \frac{1}{8} = \frac{7}{8}$$

Record your fractions.
Add. Write an equation.

2

$$\frac{2}{4} + \frac{4}{8} + \frac{1}{2} = 1\frac{1}{2}$$

Record the other team's
fractions and equation.

3

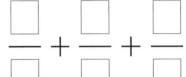

$$\frac{1}{4} + \frac{2}{4} + \frac{1}{8} = \frac{7}{8}$$

$$\frac{2}{4} + \frac{4}{8} + \frac{1}{2} = \left(1\frac{1}{2}\right)$$

Circle the greater sum.

Game 1	**Your Team**	**Other Team**
	$\dfrac{\square}{\square} + \dfrac{\square}{\square} + \dfrac{\square}{\square}$	$\dfrac{\square}{\square} + \dfrac{\square}{\square} + \dfrac{\square}{\square}$
	Equation:	Equation:
Game 2	**Your Team**	**Other Team**
	$\dfrac{\square}{\square} + \dfrac{\square}{\square} + \dfrac{\square}{\square}$	$\dfrac{\square}{\square} + \dfrac{\square}{\square} + \dfrac{\square}{\square}$
	Equation:	Equation:

Home Note: Your child practices adding and comparing fractions by playing a game.

Show What You Know

DIRECTIONS

➤ Make an estimate.

➤ Write sequences of equivalent fractions.

➤ Rewrite the problem. Write the answer in lowest terms.

➤ Compare your answer to your estimate.

① $\frac{1}{2} - \frac{2}{5} =$

② $\frac{1}{3} + \frac{1}{8} =$

③ $\frac{5}{6} - \frac{1}{3} =$

④ $\frac{1}{4} + \frac{5}{6} =$

Home Note: Your child uses sequences to get common denominators and then adds and subtracts fractions.

Compute & Compare with Cards B

DIRECTIONS

1

$$\frac{\boxed{2}}{\boxed{4}} + \frac{\boxed{1}}{\boxed{2}}$$

$$\frac{2}{4} + \frac{1}{2} = 1$$

Record your fractions.
Add. Write an equation.

2

$$\frac{\boxed{1}}{\boxed{4}} + \frac{\boxed{1}}{\boxed{8}}$$

$$\frac{1}{4} + \frac{1}{8} = \frac{3}{8}$$

Record the other team's
fractions and equation.

3

$$\frac{2}{4} + \frac{1}{2} = \boxed{1} \qquad \frac{1}{4} + \frac{1}{8} = \frac{3}{8}$$

Circle the greater sum.

Game 1	Your Team	Other Team
	$$\frac{\Box}{\Box} + \frac{\Box}{\Box}$$	$$\frac{\Box}{\Box} + \frac{\Box}{\Box}$$
	Equation:	Equation:
Game 2	**Your Team**	**Other Team**
	$$\frac{\Box}{\Box} + \frac{\Box}{\Box}$$	$$\frac{\Box}{\Box} + \frac{\Box}{\Box}$$
	Equation:	Equation:

Home Note: Your child practices adding and comparing fractions by playing a game.

Compute & Compare with Cards B

DIRECTIONS

1

$$\frac{1}{4} + \frac{2}{4} + \frac{1}{8}$$

$$\frac{1}{4} + \frac{2}{4} + \frac{1}{8} = \frac{7}{8}$$

Record your fractions.
Add. Write an equation.

2

$$\frac{2}{4} + \frac{4}{8} + \frac{1}{2}$$

$$\frac{2}{4} + \frac{4}{8} + \frac{1}{2} = 1\frac{1}{2}$$

Record the other team's
fractions and equation.

3

$$\frac{1}{4} + \frac{2}{4} + \frac{1}{8} = \frac{7}{8}$$

$$\frac{2}{4} + \frac{4}{8} + \frac{1}{2} = \boxed{1\frac{1}{2}}$$

Circle the greater sum.

Game 1	Your Team	Other Team
	$$\frac{\square}{\square} + \frac{\square}{\square} + \frac{\square}{\square}$$	$$\frac{\square}{\square} + \frac{\square}{\square} + \frac{\square}{\square}$$
	Equation:	Equation:
Game 2	Your Team	Other Team
	$$\frac{\square}{\square} + \frac{\square}{\square} + \frac{\square}{\square}$$	$$\frac{\square}{\square} + \frac{\square}{\square} + \frac{\square}{\square}$$
	Equation:	Equation:

Home Note: Your child practices adding and comparing fractions by playing a game.

Possible Addition Problems for 1, 2, 2, 3, 4, 8

➤ Complete this page as your teacher directs.

Team 2

1 2 2 3 4 8

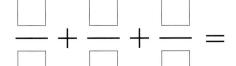

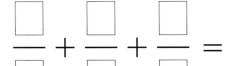

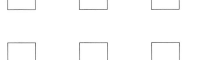

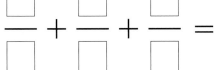

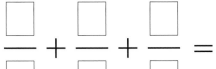

Home Note: Your child practices adding and comparing fractions.

Compute & Compare with Cards C

DIRECTIONS

1

$$\boxed{1} \quad \boxed{1} \quad \boxed{6}$$
$$\overline{\boxed{3}} + \overline{\boxed{3}} + \overline{\boxed{8}}$$

$$\frac{1}{3} + \frac{1}{3} + \frac{6}{8} = 1\frac{5}{12}$$

Record your fractions.
Add. Write an equation.

2

$$\boxed{1} \quad \boxed{2} \quad \boxed{4}$$
$$\overline{\boxed{2}} + \overline{\boxed{3}} + \overline{\boxed{8}}$$

$$\frac{1}{2} + \frac{2}{3} + \frac{4}{8} = 1\frac{2}{3}$$

Record the other team's
fractions and equation.

3

$$\frac{1}{3} + \frac{1}{3} + \frac{6}{8} = 1\frac{5}{12}$$

$$\frac{1}{2} + \frac{2}{3} + \frac{4}{8} = \boxed{1\frac{2}{3}}$$

Circle the greater answer.

Game 1	Your Team	Other Team
	$$\overline{\square} + \overline{\square} + \overline{\square}$$ Equation:	$$\overline{\square} + \overline{\square} + \overline{\square}$$ Equation:
Game 2	Your Team	Other Team
	$$\overline{\square} + \overline{\square} + \overline{\square}$$ Equation:	$$\overline{\square} + \overline{\square} + \overline{\square}$$ Equation:

Home Note: Your child practices adding and comparing fractions by playing a game.

Compute & Compare with Cards C

DIRECTIONS

1

$$\frac{\boxed{1}}{\boxed{3}} + \frac{\boxed{1}}{\boxed{3}} + \frac{\boxed{6}}{\boxed{8}}$$

$$\frac{1}{3} + \frac{1}{3} + \frac{6}{8} = 1\frac{5}{12}$$

Record your fractions.
Add. Write an equation.

2

$$\frac{\boxed{1}}{\boxed{2}} + \frac{\boxed{2}}{\boxed{3}} + \frac{\boxed{4}}{\boxed{8}}$$

$$\frac{1}{2} + \frac{2}{3} + \frac{4}{8} = 1\frac{2}{3}$$

Record the other team's
fractions and equation.

3

$$\frac{1}{3} + \frac{1}{3} + \frac{6}{8} = 1\frac{5}{12}$$

$$\frac{1}{2} + \frac{2}{3} + \frac{4}{8} = \boxed{1\frac{2}{3}}$$

Circle the greater answer.

Game 1	Your Team	Other Team
	$$\frac{\Box}{\Box} + \frac{\Box}{\Box} + \frac{\Box}{\Box}$$	$$\frac{\Box}{\Box} + \frac{\Box}{\Box} + \frac{\Box}{\Box}$$
	Equation:	Equation:
Game 2	Your Team	Other Team
	$$\frac{\Box}{\Box} + \frac{\Box}{\Box} + \frac{\Box}{\Box}$$	$$\frac{\Box}{\Box} + \frac{\Box}{\Box} + \frac{\Box}{\Box}$$
	Equation:	Equation:

Home Note: Your child practices adding and comparing fractions by playing a game.

Subtract

DIRECTIONS

1

$\boxed{<1}$

$1\frac{3}{8} - \frac{3}{4} =$

Make an estimate.

2

$1\frac{3}{8} - \frac{3}{4} =$

$1\frac{3}{8} - \frac{6}{8}$ $\boxed{<1}$

Rewrite the problem so there is a common denominator.

3

$1\frac{3}{8} - \frac{3}{4} =$

$1\frac{3}{8} - \frac{6}{8}$ $\boxed{<1}$

$\frac{11}{8} - \frac{6}{8} = \frac{5}{8}$

Rename the mixed number as a fraction and subtract.

---

① $1\frac{1}{3} - \frac{5}{6}$

② $1\frac{1}{4} - \frac{7}{8} =$

③ $1\frac{3}{16} - \frac{5}{8} =$

④ $1\frac{1}{3} - \frac{3}{4} =$

Home Note: Your child practices subtracting and comparing fractions.

Compute & Compare with Cards C

DIRECTIONS

1

$$\frac{1}{3} + \frac{1}{3} + \frac{6}{8} = 1\frac{5}{12}$$

Record your fractions.
Add. Write an equation.

2

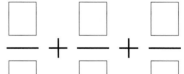

$$\frac{1}{2} + \frac{2}{3} + \frac{4}{8} = 1\frac{2}{3}$$

Record the other team's
fractions and equation.

3

$$\frac{1}{3} + \frac{1}{3} + \frac{6}{8} = 1\frac{5}{12}$$

$$\frac{1}{2} + \frac{2}{3} + \frac{4}{8} = \boxed{1\frac{2}{3}}$$

Circle the greater answer.

Game 1

Your Team

$$\frac{\Box}{\Box} + \frac{\Box}{\Box} + \frac{\Box}{\Box}$$

Equation:

Other Team

$$\frac{\Box}{\Box} + \frac{\Box}{\Box} + \frac{\Box}{\Box}$$

Equation:

Game 2

Your Team

$$\frac{\Box}{\Box} + \frac{\Box}{\Box} + \frac{\Box}{\Box}$$

Equation:

Other Team

$$\frac{\Box}{\Box} + \frac{\Box}{\Box} + \frac{\Box}{\Box}$$

Equation:

Home Note: Your child practices adding and comparing fractions by playing a game.

Compute & Compare Practice

| 1 | 2 | 3 | 8 |

> Write the problem that you and your partner will solve.

$$1\frac{\square}{\square} - \frac{\square}{\square}$$

Work Area

Home Note: Your child practices subtracting from mixed numbers.

Compute & Compare with Cards C

1

$1 \dfrac{\boxed{4}}{\boxed{8}} - \dfrac{\boxed{1}}{\boxed{3}}$

$1\frac{4}{8} - \frac{1}{3} = 1\frac{1}{6}$

Choose a problem you think
will give the greatest answer.
Record your fractions.
Subtract.
Write an equation.

2

$1 \dfrac{\boxed{6}}{\boxed{8}} - \dfrac{\boxed{2}}{\boxed{4}}$

$1\frac{6}{8} - \frac{2}{4} = 1\frac{1}{4}$

Record the other team's
fractions and equation.

3

$1\frac{4}{8} - \frac{1}{3} = 1\frac{1}{6}$

$1\frac{6}{8} - \frac{2}{4} = \boxed{1\frac{1}{4}}$

Circle the greater answer.

Game 1	Your Team	Other Team
	$1 \dfrac{\square}{\square} - \dfrac{\square}{\square}$	$1 \dfrac{\square}{\square} - \dfrac{\square}{\square}$
	Equation:	Equation:
Game 2	**Your Team**	**Other Team**
	$1 \dfrac{\square}{\square} - \dfrac{\square}{\square}$	$1 \dfrac{\square}{\square} - \dfrac{\square}{\square}$
	Equation:	Equation:

Home Note: Your child practices subtracting and comparing fractions by playing a game.

Compute & Compare with Cards C

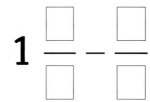

$$1\frac{\square}{\square} - \frac{\square}{\square}$$

Team 1's Cards	**Team 2's Cards**
1 3 6 8	1 3 3 4

Work Area	**Work Area**

Team 1's Score

Team 2's Score

Home Note: Your child practices subtracting and comparing fractions.

Compute & Compare with Cards C

DIRECTIONS

1

$$1\frac{\boxed{4}}{\boxed{8}} - \frac{\boxed{1}}{\boxed{3}}$$

$$1\frac{4}{8} - \frac{1}{3} = 1\frac{1}{6}$$

Choose a problem you think will give the greatest answer.
Record your fractions.
Subtract.
Write an equation.

2

$$1\frac{\boxed{6}}{\boxed{8}} - \frac{\boxed{2}}{\boxed{4}}$$

$$1\frac{6}{8} - \frac{2}{4} = 1\frac{1}{4}$$

Record the other team's fractions and equation.

3

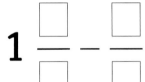

$$1\frac{6}{8} - \frac{2}{4} = \boxed{1\frac{1}{4}}$$

Circle the greater answer.

Game 1	Your Team	Other Team
	$1\dfrac{\square}{\square} - \dfrac{\square}{\square}$	$1\dfrac{\square}{\square} - \dfrac{\square}{\square}$
	Equation:	Equation:
Game 2	Your Team	Other Team
	$1\dfrac{\square}{\square} - \dfrac{\square}{\square}$	$1\dfrac{\square}{\square} - \dfrac{\square}{\square}$
	Equation:	Equation:

Home Note: Your child practices subtracting and comparing fractions by playing a game.

Lesson 24

Compute & Compare with Cards C

DIRECTIONS

1

$$1\frac{\boxed{4}}{\boxed{8}} - \frac{\boxed{1}}{\boxed{3}}$$

$$1\frac{4}{8} - \frac{1}{3} = 1\frac{1}{6}$$

Choose a problem you think will give the greatest answer.
Record your fractions.
Subtract.
Write an equation.

2

$$1\frac{\boxed{6}}{\boxed{8}} - \frac{\boxed{2}}{\boxed{4}}$$

$$1\frac{6}{8} - \frac{2}{4} = 1\frac{1}{4}$$

Record the other team's fractions and equation.

3

$$1\frac{4}{8} - \frac{1}{3} = 1\frac{1}{6}$$

$$1\frac{6}{8} - \frac{2}{4} = \boxed{1\frac{1}{4}}$$

Circle the greater answer.

Game 1	Your Team	Other Team
	$1\frac{\Box}{\Box} - \frac{\Box}{\Box}$	$1\frac{\Box}{\Box} - \frac{\Box}{\Box}$
	Equation:	Equation:
Game 2	Your Team	Other Team
	$1\frac{\Box}{\Box} - \frac{\Box}{\Box}$	$1\frac{\Box}{\Box} - \frac{\Box}{\Box}$
	Equation:	Equation:

 **Home Note:** Your child practices subtracting and comparing fractions by playing a game.

Show What You Know

➤ Figure out each answer.

➤ Write an equation with the answer in lowest terms.

➤ You may use your *Equivalent Fractions Sequences* chart on page 23.

---

①   **Work Area**

$$\frac{6}{8} + \frac{3}{4} + \frac{1}{3}$$

Equation:

---

②   **Work Area**

$$\frac{1}{4} + \frac{2}{3} + \frac{3}{4}$$

Equation:

---

③   **Work Area**

$$\frac{1}{6} + \frac{6}{8} + \frac{1}{3}$$

Equation:

Home Note: Your child adds fractions and simplifies sums.

Show What You Know

➤ Solve the following problems.

➤ Write your answer in lowest terms or simplest form.

---

④ $1\frac{1}{3} - \frac{2}{6} =$ **Work Area**

Equation:

---

⑤ $1\frac{5}{6} - \frac{2}{3} =$ **Work Area**

Equation:

---

⑥ $1\frac{1}{4} - \frac{3}{8} =$ **Work Area**

Equation:

---

⑦ $1\frac{7}{16} - \frac{2}{4} =$ **Work Area**

Equation:

---

⑧ $1\frac{3}{4} - \frac{9}{16} =$ **Work Area**

Equation:

     Home Note: Your child subtracts fractions and simplifies answers.

Compute & Compare with Cards C

DIRECTIONS

1

$$\frac{\boxed{1}}{\boxed{3}} + \frac{\boxed{1}}{\boxed{3}} + \frac{\boxed{6}}{\boxed{8}}$$

$$\frac{1}{3} + \frac{1}{3} + \frac{6}{8} = 1\frac{5}{12}$$

Record your fractions.
Add. Write an equation.

2

$$\frac{\boxed{1}}{\boxed{2}} + \frac{\boxed{2}}{\boxed{3}} + \frac{\boxed{4}}{\boxed{8}}$$

$$\frac{1}{2} + \frac{2}{3} + \frac{4}{8} = 1\frac{2}{3}$$

Record the other team's
fractions and equation.

3

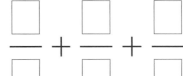

$$\frac{1}{3} + \frac{1}{3} + \frac{6}{8} = 1\frac{5}{12}$$

$$\frac{1}{2} + \frac{2}{3} + \frac{4}{8} = \boxed{1\frac{2}{3}}$$

Circle the greater answer.

	Your Team	**Other Team**
Game 1	$\dfrac{\Box}{\Box} + \dfrac{\Box}{\Box} + \dfrac{\Box}{\Box}$ Equation:	$\dfrac{\Box}{\Box} + \dfrac{\Box}{\Box} + \dfrac{\Box}{\Box}$ Equation:
Game 2	$\dfrac{\Box}{\Box} + \dfrac{\Box}{\Box} + \dfrac{\Box}{\Box}$ Equation:	$\dfrac{\Box}{\Box} + \dfrac{\Box}{\Box} + \dfrac{\Box}{\Box}$ Equation:

Home Note: Your child practices adding and comparing fractions by playing a game.

Compute & Compare with Cards C

DIRECTIONS

1

$$1\frac{\boxed{4}}{\boxed{8}} - \frac{\boxed{1}}{\boxed{3}}$$

$$1\frac{4}{8} - \frac{1}{3} = 1\frac{1}{6}$$

Choose a problem you think will give the greatest answer.
Record your fractions.
Subtract.
Write an equation.

2

$$1\frac{\boxed{6}}{\boxed{8}} - \frac{\boxed{2}}{\boxed{4}}$$

$$1\frac{6}{8} - \frac{2}{4} = 1\frac{1}{4}$$

Record the other team's fractions and equation.

3

$$1\frac{4}{8} - \frac{1}{3} = 1\frac{1}{6}$$

$$1\frac{6}{8} - \frac{2}{4} = \boxed{1\frac{1}{4}}$$

Circle the greater answer.

Game 1	Your Team	Other Team
	$1\frac{\boxed{}}{\boxed{}} - \frac{\boxed{}}{\boxed{}}$	$1\frac{\boxed{}}{\boxed{}} - \frac{\boxed{}}{\boxed{}}$
	Equation:	Equation:

Game 2	Your Team	Other Team
	$1\frac{\boxed{}}{\boxed{}} - \frac{\boxed{}}{\boxed{}}$	$1\frac{\boxed{}}{\boxed{}} - \frac{\boxed{}}{\boxed{}}$
	Equation:	Equation:

Home Note: Your child practices adding and comparing fractions by playing a game.

Pizza by the Slice
Mix and Match

Cheese $\frac{1}{2}$ $\frac{1}{2}$

Pepperoni $\frac{1}{3}$ $\frac{1}{3}$ $\frac{1}{3}$

Mushroom $\frac{1}{4}$ $\frac{1}{4}$ $\frac{1}{4}$ $\frac{1}{4}$

Sausage $\frac{1}{5}$ $\frac{1}{5}$ $\frac{1}{5}$ $\frac{1}{5}$ $\frac{1}{5}$

Hamburger $\frac{1}{6}$ $\frac{1}{6}$ $\frac{1}{6}$ $\frac{1}{6}$ $\frac{1}{6}$ $\frac{1}{6}$

Olive $\frac{1}{8}$ $\frac{1}{8}$ $\frac{1}{8}$ $\frac{1}{8}$ $\frac{1}{8}$ $\frac{1}{8}$ $\frac{1}{8}$ $\frac{1}{8}$

Home Note: Your child uses a story about pizza to add fractions.

Lesson 26

53

One Whole Pizza Problem

Order

1 cheese

1 mushroom

2 olive

1

Order Form							
Cheese	$\frac{1}{2}$	$\frac{1}{2}$					
Pepperoni	$\frac{1}{3}$	$\frac{1}{3}$	$\frac{1}{3}$				
Mushroom	$\frac{1}{4}$	$\frac{1}{4}$	$\frac{1}{4}$	$\frac{1}{4}$			
Sausage	$\frac{1}{5}$	$\frac{1}{5}$	$\frac{1}{5}$	$\frac{1}{5}$	$\frac{1}{5}$		
Hamburger	$\frac{1}{6}$	$\frac{1}{6}$	$\frac{1}{6}$	$\frac{1}{6}$	$\frac{1}{6}$	$\frac{1}{6}$	
Olive	$\frac{1}{8}$	$\frac{1}{8}$	$\frac{1}{8}$	$\frac{1}{8}$	$\frac{1}{8}$	$\frac{1}{8}$	$\frac{1}{8}$ $\frac{1}{8}$

Circle the order.

2

$$\frac{1}{2} + \frac{1}{4} + \frac{2}{8} =$$

Write the problem.

3

$$\frac{1}{2} + \frac{1}{4} + \frac{2}{8} =$$
$$\frac{2}{4} + \frac{1}{4} + \frac{1}{4} = \frac{4}{4} = 1$$

Solve the problem.

1

Order Form							
Cheese	$\frac{1}{2}$	$\frac{1}{2}$					
Pepperoni	$\frac{1}{3}$	$\frac{1}{3}$	$\frac{1}{3}$				
Mushroom	$\frac{1}{4}$	$\frac{1}{4}$	$\frac{1}{4}$	$\frac{1}{4}$			
Sausage	$\frac{1}{5}$	$\frac{1}{5}$	$\frac{1}{5}$	$\frac{1}{5}$	$\frac{1}{5}$		
Hamburger	$\frac{1}{6}$	$\frac{1}{6}$	$\frac{1}{6}$	$\frac{1}{6}$	$\frac{1}{6}$	$\frac{1}{6}$	
Olive	$\frac{1}{8}$	$\frac{1}{8}$	$\frac{1}{8}$	$\frac{1}{8}$	$\frac{1}{8}$	$\frac{1}{8}$	$\frac{1}{8}$ $\frac{1}{8}$

Write the problem.

Solve the problem.

2

Order Form							
Cheese	$\frac{1}{2}$	$\frac{1}{2}$					
Pepperoni	$\frac{1}{3}$	$\frac{1}{3}$	$\frac{1}{3}$				
Mushroom	$\frac{1}{4}$	$\frac{1}{4}$	$\frac{1}{4}$	$\frac{1}{4}$			
Sausage	$\frac{1}{5}$	$\frac{1}{5}$	$\frac{1}{5}$	$\frac{1}{5}$	$\frac{1}{5}$		
Hamburger	$\frac{1}{6}$	$\frac{1}{6}$	$\frac{1}{6}$	$\frac{1}{6}$	$\frac{1}{6}$	$\frac{1}{6}$	
Olive	$\frac{1}{8}$	$\frac{1}{8}$	$\frac{1}{8}$	$\frac{1}{8}$	$\frac{1}{8}$	$\frac{1}{8}$	$\frac{1}{8}$ $\frac{1}{8}$

Write the problem.

Solve the problem.

3

Order Form							
Cheese	$\frac{1}{2}$	$\frac{1}{2}$					
Pepperoni	$\frac{1}{3}$	$\frac{1}{3}$	$\frac{1}{3}$				
Mushroom	$\frac{1}{4}$	$\frac{1}{4}$	$\frac{1}{4}$	$\frac{1}{4}$			
Sausage	$\frac{1}{5}$	$\frac{1}{5}$	$\frac{1}{5}$	$\frac{1}{5}$	$\frac{1}{5}$		
Hamburger	$\frac{1}{6}$	$\frac{1}{6}$	$\frac{1}{6}$	$\frac{1}{6}$	$\frac{1}{6}$	$\frac{1}{6}$	
Olive	$\frac{1}{8}$	$\frac{1}{8}$	$\frac{1}{8}$	$\frac{1}{8}$	$\frac{1}{8}$	$\frac{1}{8}$	$\frac{1}{8}$ $\frac{1}{8}$

Write the problem.

Solve the problem.

Home Note: Your child identifies combinations of fractions that have the sum 1.

Fractions that Add to One Whole

Order

1 mushroom

6 olive

1

Order Form

Cheese	$\frac{1}{2}$	$\frac{1}{2}$					
Pepperoni	$\frac{1}{3}$	$\frac{1}{3}$	$\frac{1}{3}$				
Mushroom	$\left(\frac{1}{4}\right)$	$\frac{1}{4}$	$\frac{1}{4}$	$\frac{1}{4}$			
Sausage	$\frac{1}{5}$	$\frac{1}{5}$	$\frac{1}{5}$	$\frac{1}{5}$	$\frac{1}{5}$		
Hamburger	$\frac{1}{6}$	$\frac{1}{6}$	$\frac{1}{6}$	$\frac{1}{6}$	$\frac{1}{6}$	$\frac{1}{6}$	
Olive	$\left(\frac{1}{8}\right)$	$\left(\frac{1}{8}\right)$	$\left(\frac{1}{8}\right)$	$\left(\frac{1}{8}\right)$	$\left(\frac{1}{8}\right)$	$\left(\frac{1}{8}\right)$	$\frac{1}{8}$	$\frac{1}{8}$

Circle an order for one whole pizza.

2

$\frac{1}{4} + \frac{1}{8} + \frac{1}{8} + \frac{1}{8} + \frac{1}{8} + \frac{1}{8} + \frac{1}{8} =$

Write the problem.

3

$\frac{1}{4} + \frac{1}{8} + \frac{1}{8} + \frac{1}{8} + \frac{1}{8} + \frac{1}{8} + \frac{1}{8} =$

$\frac{1}{4} + \frac{6}{8} =$

$\frac{1}{4} + \frac{3}{4} = 1$

Solve the problem.

---

① Order Form

Cheese	$\frac{1}{2}$	$\frac{1}{2}$					
Pepperoni	$\frac{1}{3}$	$\frac{1}{3}$	$\frac{1}{3}$				
Mushroom	$\frac{1}{4}$	$\frac{1}{4}$	$\frac{1}{4}$	$\frac{1}{4}$			
Sausage	$\frac{1}{5}$	$\frac{1}{5}$	$\frac{1}{5}$	$\frac{1}{5}$	$\frac{1}{5}$		
Hamburger	$\frac{1}{6}$	$\frac{1}{6}$	$\frac{1}{6}$	$\frac{1}{6}$	$\frac{1}{6}$	$\frac{1}{6}$	
Olive	$\frac{1}{8}$	$\frac{1}{8}$	$\frac{1}{8}$	$\frac{1}{8}$	$\frac{1}{8}$	$\frac{1}{8}$	$\frac{1}{8}$	$\frac{1}{8}$

Write the problem.

Solve the problem.

---

② Order Form

Cheese	$\frac{1}{2}$	$\frac{1}{2}$					
Pepperoni	$\frac{1}{3}$	$\frac{1}{3}$	$\frac{1}{3}$				
Mushroom	$\frac{1}{4}$	$\frac{1}{4}$	$\frac{1}{4}$	$\frac{1}{4}$			
Sausage	$\frac{1}{5}$	$\frac{1}{5}$	$\frac{1}{5}$	$\frac{1}{5}$	$\frac{1}{5}$		
Hamburger	$\frac{1}{6}$	$\frac{1}{6}$	$\frac{1}{6}$	$\frac{1}{6}$	$\frac{1}{6}$	$\frac{1}{6}$	
Olive	$\frac{1}{8}$	$\frac{1}{8}$	$\frac{1}{8}$	$\frac{1}{8}$	$\frac{1}{8}$	$\frac{1}{8}$	$\frac{1}{8}$	$\frac{1}{8}$

Write the problem.

Solve the problem.

---

③ Order Form

Cheese	$\frac{1}{2}$	$\frac{1}{2}$					
Pepperoni	$\frac{1}{3}$	$\frac{1}{3}$	$\frac{1}{3}$				
Mushroom	$\frac{1}{4}$	$\frac{1}{4}$	$\frac{1}{4}$	$\frac{1}{4}$			
Sausage	$\frac{1}{5}$	$\frac{1}{5}$	$\frac{1}{5}$	$\frac{1}{5}$	$\frac{1}{5}$		
Hamburger	$\frac{1}{6}$	$\frac{1}{6}$	$\frac{1}{6}$	$\frac{1}{6}$	$\frac{1}{6}$	$\frac{1}{6}$	
Olive	$\frac{1}{8}$	$\frac{1}{8}$	$\frac{1}{8}$	$\frac{1}{8}$	$\frac{1}{8}$	$\frac{1}{8}$	$\frac{1}{8}$	$\frac{1}{8}$

Write the problem.

Solve the problem.

Home Note: Your child identifies combinations of fractions that have the sum 1.

Pizza by the Slice

Order

1 mushroom

1 hamburger

1

Order Form							
Cheese	$\frac{1}{2}$	$\frac{1}{2}$					
Pepperoni	$\frac{1}{3}$	$\frac{1}{3}$	$\frac{1}{3}$				
Mushroom	⟨$\frac{1}{4}$⟩	$\frac{1}{4}$	$\frac{1}{4}$	$\frac{1}{4}$			
Sausage	$\frac{1}{5}$	$\frac{1}{5}$	$\frac{1}{5}$	$\frac{1}{5}$	$\frac{1}{5}$		
Hamburger	⟨$\frac{1}{6}$⟩	$\frac{1}{6}$	$\frac{1}{6}$	$\frac{1}{6}$	$\frac{1}{6}$	$\frac{1}{6}$	
Olive	$\frac{1}{8}$	$\frac{1}{8}$	$\frac{1}{8}$	$\frac{1}{8}$	$\frac{1}{8}$	$\frac{1}{8}$	$\frac{1}{8}$ $\frac{1}{8}$

Circle the order.

2

$$\frac{1}{4} + \frac{1}{6}$$

Write the problem.

3

$$\frac{1}{4} + \frac{1}{6} =$$
$$\frac{3}{12} + \frac{2}{12} = \frac{5}{12}$$

Solve the problem.

1

Order Form							
Cheese	$\frac{1}{2}$	$\frac{1}{2}$					
Pepperoni	$\frac{1}{3}$	$\frac{1}{3}$	$\frac{1}{3}$				
Mushroom	$\frac{1}{4}$	$\frac{1}{4}$	$\frac{1}{4}$	$\frac{1}{4}$			
Sausage	$\frac{1}{5}$	$\frac{1}{5}$	$\frac{1}{5}$	$\frac{1}{5}$	$\frac{1}{5}$		
Hamburger	$\frac{1}{6}$	$\frac{1}{6}$	$\frac{1}{6}$	$\frac{1}{6}$	$\frac{1}{6}$	$\frac{1}{6}$	
Olive	$\frac{1}{8}$	$\frac{1}{8}$	$\frac{1}{8}$	$\frac{1}{8}$	$\frac{1}{8}$	$\frac{1}{8}$	$\frac{1}{8}$ $\frac{1}{8}$

Write the problem.

Solve the problem.

2

Order Form							
Cheese	$\frac{1}{2}$	$\frac{1}{2}$					
Pepperoni	$\frac{1}{3}$	$\frac{1}{3}$	$\frac{1}{3}$				
Mushroom	$\frac{1}{4}$	$\frac{1}{4}$	$\frac{1}{4}$	$\frac{1}{4}$			
Sausage	$\frac{1}{5}$	$\frac{1}{5}$	$\frac{1}{5}$	$\frac{1}{5}$	$\frac{1}{5}$		
Hamburger	$\frac{1}{6}$	$\frac{1}{6}$	$\frac{1}{6}$	$\frac{1}{6}$	$\frac{1}{6}$	$\frac{1}{6}$	
Olive	$\frac{1}{8}$	$\frac{1}{8}$	$\frac{1}{8}$	$\frac{1}{8}$	$\frac{1}{8}$	$\frac{1}{8}$	$\frac{1}{8}$ $\frac{1}{8}$

Write the problem.

Solve the problem.

3

Order Form							
Cheese	$\frac{1}{2}$	$\frac{1}{2}$					
Pepperoni	$\frac{1}{3}$	$\frac{1}{3}$	$\frac{1}{3}$				
Mushroom	$\frac{1}{4}$	$\frac{1}{4}$	$\frac{1}{4}$	$\frac{1}{4}$			
Sausage	$\frac{1}{5}$	$\frac{1}{5}$	$\frac{1}{5}$	$\frac{1}{5}$	$\frac{1}{5}$		
Hamburger	$\frac{1}{6}$	$\frac{1}{6}$	$\frac{1}{6}$	$\frac{1}{6}$	$\frac{1}{6}$	$\frac{1}{6}$	
Olive	$\frac{1}{8}$	$\frac{1}{8}$	$\frac{1}{8}$	$\frac{1}{8}$	$\frac{1}{8}$	$\frac{1}{8}$	$\frac{1}{8}$ $\frac{1}{8}$

Write the problem.

Solve the problem.

Home Note: Your child identifies combinations of fractions that have sums less than 1.

Pizza by the Slice

Order
1 mushroom
1 hamburger

1

Order Form							
Cheese	$\frac{1}{2}$	$\frac{1}{2}$					
Pepperoni	$\frac{1}{3}$	$\frac{1}{3}$	$\frac{1}{3}$				
Mushroom	$\boxed{\frac{1}{4}}$	$\frac{1}{4}$	$\frac{1}{4}$	$\frac{1}{4}$			
Sausage	$\frac{1}{5}$	$\frac{1}{5}$	$\frac{1}{5}$	$\frac{1}{5}$	$\frac{1}{5}$		
Hamburger	$\boxed{\frac{1}{6}}$	$\frac{1}{6}$	$\frac{1}{6}$	$\frac{1}{6}$	$\frac{1}{6}$	$\frac{1}{6}$	
Olive	$\frac{1}{8}$	$\frac{1}{8}$	$\frac{1}{8}$	$\frac{1}{8}$	$\frac{1}{8}$	$\frac{1}{8}$	$\frac{1}{8}$ $\frac{1}{8}$

Circle the order.

2

$$\frac{1}{4} + \frac{1}{6}$$

Write the problem.

3

$$\frac{1}{4} + \frac{1}{6} =$$
$$\frac{3}{12} + \frac{2}{12} = \frac{5}{12}$$

Solve the problem.

---

① Order Form

Cheese	$\frac{1}{2}$	$\frac{1}{2}$					
Pepperoni	$\frac{1}{3}$	$\frac{1}{3}$	$\frac{1}{3}$				
Mushroom	$\frac{1}{4}$	$\frac{1}{4}$	$\frac{1}{4}$	$\frac{1}{4}$			
Sausage	$\frac{1}{5}$	$\frac{1}{5}$	$\frac{1}{5}$	$\frac{1}{5}$	$\frac{1}{5}$		
Hamburger	$\frac{1}{6}$	$\frac{1}{6}$	$\frac{1}{6}$	$\frac{1}{6}$	$\frac{1}{6}$	$\frac{1}{6}$	
Olive	$\frac{1}{8}$	$\frac{1}{8}$	$\frac{1}{8}$	$\frac{1}{8}$	$\frac{1}{8}$	$\frac{1}{8}$	$\frac{1}{8}$ $\frac{1}{8}$

Write the problem.

Solve the problem.

---

② Order Form

Cheese	$\frac{1}{2}$	$\frac{1}{2}$					
Pepperoni	$\frac{1}{3}$	$\frac{1}{3}$	$\frac{1}{3}$				
Mushroom	$\frac{1}{4}$	$\frac{1}{4}$	$\frac{1}{4}$	$\frac{1}{4}$			
Sausage	$\frac{1}{5}$	$\frac{1}{5}$	$\frac{1}{5}$	$\frac{1}{5}$	$\frac{1}{5}$		
Hamburger	$\frac{1}{6}$	$\frac{1}{6}$	$\frac{1}{6}$	$\frac{1}{6}$	$\frac{1}{6}$	$\frac{1}{6}$	
Olive	$\frac{1}{8}$	$\frac{1}{8}$	$\frac{1}{8}$	$\frac{1}{8}$	$\frac{1}{8}$	$\frac{1}{8}$	$\frac{1}{8}$ $\frac{1}{8}$

Write the problem.

Solve the problem.

---

③ Order Form

Cheese	$\frac{1}{2}$	$\frac{1}{2}$					
Pepperoni	$\frac{1}{3}$	$\frac{1}{3}$	$\frac{1}{3}$				
Mushroom	$\frac{1}{4}$	$\frac{1}{4}$	$\frac{1}{4}$	$\frac{1}{4}$			
Sausage	$\frac{1}{5}$	$\frac{1}{5}$	$\frac{1}{5}$	$\frac{1}{5}$	$\frac{1}{5}$		
Hamburger	$\frac{1}{6}$	$\frac{1}{6}$	$\frac{1}{6}$	$\frac{1}{6}$	$\frac{1}{6}$	$\frac{1}{6}$	
Olive	$\frac{1}{8}$	$\frac{1}{8}$	$\frac{1}{8}$	$\frac{1}{8}$	$\frac{1}{8}$	$\frac{1}{8}$	$\frac{1}{8}$ $\frac{1}{8}$

Write the problem.

Solve the problem.

Home Note: Your child identifies combinations of fractions that have sums less than 1.

Solving Word Problems

Maria ordered 2 slices of hamburger pizza and 1 slice of sausage pizza. How much pizza did Maria order?

1

Order Form

Cheese	$\frac{1}{2}$	$\frac{1}{2}$					
Pepperoni	$\frac{1}{3}$	$\frac{1}{3}$	$\frac{1}{3}$				
Mushroom	$\frac{1}{4}$	$\frac{1}{4}$	$\frac{1}{4}$	$\frac{1}{4}$			
Sausage	$\frac{1}{5}$	$\frac{1}{5}$	$\frac{1}{5}$	$\frac{1}{5}$	$\frac{1}{5}$		
Hamburger	$\frac{1}{6}$	$\frac{1}{6}$	$\frac{1}{6}$	$\frac{1}{6}$	$\frac{1}{6}$	$\frac{1}{6}$	
Olive	$\frac{1}{8}$	$\frac{1}{8}$	$\frac{1}{8}$	$\frac{1}{8}$	$\frac{1}{8}$	$\frac{1}{8}$	$\frac{1}{8}$ $\frac{1}{8}$

Circle the order.

2

$$\frac{1}{6} + \frac{1}{6} + \frac{1}{5}$$

Write the problem.

3

$$\frac{2}{6} + \frac{1}{5} =$$

$$\frac{1}{3}, \frac{2}{6}, \frac{3}{9}, \frac{4}{12}, \frac{5}{15}, \cdots$$

$$\frac{1}{5}, \frac{2}{10}, \frac{3}{15}, \cdots$$

$$\frac{5}{15} + \frac{3}{15} = \frac{8}{15}$$

Solve the problem.

---

1 Jordan ordered 1 slice of cheese pizza, 3 slices of mushroom pizza, and 1 slice of sausage pizza. How much pizza did Jordan order?

Write the problem.

Solve the problem.

Order Form

Cheese	$\frac{1}{2}$	$\frac{1}{2}$						
Pepperoni	$\frac{1}{3}$	$\frac{1}{3}$	$\frac{1}{3}$					
Mushroom	$\frac{1}{4}$	$\frac{1}{4}$	$\frac{1}{4}$	$\frac{1}{4}$				
Sausage	$\frac{1}{5}$	$\frac{1}{5}$	$\frac{1}{5}$	$\frac{1}{5}$	$\frac{1}{5}$			
Hamburger	$\frac{1}{6}$	$\frac{1}{6}$	$\frac{1}{6}$	$\frac{1}{6}$	$\frac{1}{6}$	$\frac{1}{6}$		
Olive	$\frac{1}{8}$	$\frac{1}{8}$	$\frac{1}{8}$	$\frac{1}{8}$	$\frac{1}{8}$	$\frac{1}{8}$	$\frac{1}{8}$	$\frac{1}{8}$

Home Note: Your child solves word problems.

Solving Word Problems

Maria ordered 2 slices of hamburger pizza and 1 slice of sausage pizza. How much pizza did Maria order?

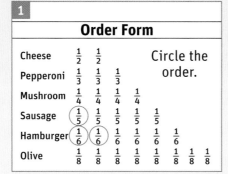

1

Order Form

Cheese	$\frac{1}{2}$	$\frac{1}{2}$			
Pepperoni	$\frac{1}{3}$	$\frac{1}{3}$	$\frac{1}{3}$		
Mushroom	$\frac{1}{4}$	$\frac{1}{4}$	$\frac{1}{4}$	$\frac{1}{4}$	
Sausage	$\frac{1}{5}$	$\frac{1}{5}$	$\frac{1}{5}$	$\frac{1}{5}$	$\frac{1}{5}$
Hamburger	$\frac{1}{6}$	$\frac{1}{6}$	$\frac{1}{6}$	$\frac{1}{6}$	$\frac{1}{6}$
Olive	$\frac{1}{8}$	$\frac{1}{8}$	$\frac{1}{8}$	$\frac{1}{8}$	$\frac{1}{8}$ $\frac{1}{8}$ $\frac{1}{8}$

Circle the order.

2

$$\frac{1}{6} + \frac{1}{6} + \frac{1}{5}$$

Write the problem.

3

$$\frac{2}{6} + \frac{1}{5} =$$
$$\frac{1}{3}, \frac{2}{6}, \frac{3}{9}, \frac{4}{12}, \frac{5}{15}, \cdots$$
$$\frac{1}{5}, \frac{2}{10}, \frac{3}{15}, \cdots$$
$$\frac{5}{15} + \frac{3}{15} = \frac{8}{15}$$

Solve the problem.

---

1 Shannon ordered 2 slices of pepperoni pizza, 1 slice of mushroom pizza, and 1 slice of hamburger pizza. How much pizza did Shannon order?

Write the problem.

Solve the problem.

Order Form

Cheese	$\frac{1}{2}$	$\frac{1}{2}$						
Pepperoni	$\frac{1}{3}$	$\frac{1}{3}$	$\frac{1}{3}$					
Mushroom	$\frac{1}{4}$	$\frac{1}{4}$	$\frac{1}{4}$	$\frac{1}{4}$				
Sausage	$\frac{1}{5}$	$\frac{1}{5}$	$\frac{1}{5}$	$\frac{1}{5}$	$\frac{1}{5}$			
Hamburger	$\frac{1}{6}$	$\frac{1}{6}$	$\frac{1}{6}$	$\frac{1}{6}$	$\frac{1}{6}$	$\frac{1}{6}$		
Olive	$\frac{1}{8}$	$\frac{1}{8}$	$\frac{1}{8}$	$\frac{1}{8}$	$\frac{1}{8}$	$\frac{1}{8}$	$\frac{1}{8}$	$\frac{1}{8}$

Home Note: Your child solves word problems.

Write and Solve Word Problems

➤ Use the *Pizza by the Slice* chart on page 53.

1   Mario's Rules
Customer must order slices from 2 kinds of pizza and must order more than 2 slices of each.

Read Mario's Rules.

2
__3__ slice(s) of __mushroom__ pizza
__4__ slice(s) of __sausage__ pizza
How much pizza did the customer order? $1\frac{11}{20}$

Write a problem.

3
$$\frac{1}{4} + \frac{1}{4} + \frac{1}{4} + \frac{1}{5} + \frac{1}{5} + \frac{1}{5} + \frac{1}{5} =$$
$$\frac{3}{4} + \frac{4}{5} =$$
$$\frac{15}{20} + \frac{16}{20} = \frac{31}{20} = 1\frac{11}{20}$$

Solve the problem.

---

①	2 kinds of pizza but no more than 5 slices of each	___ slice(s) of _____ pizza ___ slice(s) of _____ pizza **How much pizza did the customer order?** _____	
②	more than 2 kinds of pizza with a total no more than 2 whole pizzas	___ slice(s) of _____ pizza ___ slice(s) of _____ pizza ___ slice(s) of _____ pizza ___ slice(s) of _____ pizza **How much pizza did the customer order?** _____	
③	3 slices from each of 3 different pizzas	___ slice(s) of _____ pizza ___ slice(s) of _____ pizza ___ slice(s) of _____ pizza **How much pizza did the customer order?** _____	

Lesson 28

Home Note: Your child writes and solves word problems.

TM & © Scholastic Inc. All rights reserved.

Write about Fractions

➤ Tell about fractions with words, numbers, and pictures.

ABOUT FRACTIONS

Home Note: Your child writes about fractions.

Show What You Know

DIRECTIONS

➤ Make an estimate.

➤ Add or subtract.

➤ Write the answer in lowest terms.

① $\frac{5}{6} - \frac{1}{6} =$

② $\frac{9}{10} - \frac{1}{2} =$

③ $1\frac{1}{8} - \frac{5}{8} =$

④ $1\frac{2}{3} - \frac{5}{12} =$

⑤ $\frac{15}{16} - \frac{7}{16} =$

⑥ $\frac{1}{4} + \frac{7}{12} =$

⑦ $\frac{1}{2} + \frac{3}{4} =$

⑧ $\frac{4}{6} + \frac{2}{4} + \frac{1}{3} =$

⑨ $1\frac{5}{6} - \frac{1}{2} =$

⑩ $\frac{1}{6} + \frac{1}{4} + \frac{2}{8} =$

 Home Note: Your child adds and subtracts fractions and mixed numbers.

Show What You Know

DIRECTIONS

➤ Refer to the chart on page 53.

➤ Add.

➤ Write the answer in lowest terms.

1

Order Form							
Cheese	$\frac{1}{2}$	$\frac{1}{2}$					
Pepperoni	$\frac{1}{3}$	$\frac{1}{3}$	$\frac{1}{3}$				
Mushroom	$\frac{1}{4}$	$\frac{1}{4}$	$\frac{1}{4}$	$\frac{1}{4}$			
Sausage	$\frac{1}{5}$	$\frac{1}{5}$	$\frac{1}{5}$	$\frac{1}{5}$	$\frac{1}{5}$		
Hamburger	$\frac{1}{6}$	$\frac{1}{6}$	$\frac{1}{6}$	$\frac{1}{6}$	$\frac{1}{6}$	$\frac{1}{6}$	
Olive	$\frac{1}{8}$	$\frac{1}{8}$	$\frac{1}{8}$	$\frac{1}{8}$	$\frac{1}{8}$	$\frac{1}{8}$	$\frac{1}{8}$	$\frac{1}{8}$

Write the problem.

Solve the problem.

2

Order Form							
Cheese	$\frac{1}{2}$	$\frac{1}{2}$					
Pepperoni	$\frac{1}{3}$	$\frac{1}{3}$	$\frac{1}{3}$				
Mushroom	$\frac{1}{4}$	$\frac{1}{4}$	$\frac{1}{4}$	$\frac{1}{4}$			
Sausage	$\frac{1}{5}$	$\frac{1}{5}$	$\frac{1}{5}$	$\frac{1}{5}$	$\frac{1}{5}$		
Hamburger	$\frac{1}{6}$	$\frac{1}{6}$	$\frac{1}{6}$	$\frac{1}{6}$	$\frac{1}{6}$	$\frac{1}{6}$	
Olive	$\frac{1}{8}$	$\frac{1}{8}$	$\frac{1}{8}$	$\frac{1}{8}$	$\frac{1}{8}$	$\frac{1}{8}$	$\frac{1}{8}$	$\frac{1}{8}$

Write the problem.

Solve the problem.

3

Order Form							
Cheese	$\frac{1}{2}$	$\frac{1}{2}$					
Pepperoni	$\frac{1}{3}$	$\frac{1}{3}$	$\frac{1}{3}$				
Mushroom	$\frac{1}{4}$	$\frac{1}{4}$	$\frac{1}{4}$	$\frac{1}{4}$			
Sausage	$\frac{1}{5}$	$\frac{1}{5}$	$\frac{1}{5}$	$\frac{1}{5}$	$\frac{1}{5}$		
Hamburger	$\frac{1}{6}$	$\frac{1}{6}$	$\frac{1}{6}$	$\frac{1}{6}$	$\frac{1}{6}$	$\frac{1}{6}$	
Olive	$\frac{1}{8}$	$\frac{1}{8}$	$\frac{1}{8}$	$\frac{1}{8}$	$\frac{1}{8}$	$\frac{1}{8}$	$\frac{1}{8}$	$\frac{1}{8}$

Write the problem.

Solve the problem.

Home Note: Your child combines fractions that have sums other than 1.

Show What You Know

DIRECTIONS

➤ Figure each team's score.
➤ Circle the greater score.

④ Team 1

$$\frac{2}{3} + \frac{4}{6} + \frac{6}{8}$$

Equation

⑤ Team 2

$$\frac{1}{2} + \frac{3}{4} + \frac{6}{8}$$

Equation

 Home Note: Your child adds and compares fractions.

Math Vocabulary

➤ Write new words and terms in the box.

➤ Write a definition, show an example, or draw a picture for each word or term in your list.

Home Note: Your child creates a math vocabulary word list.

Math Vocabulary

➤ Write new words and terms in the box.

➤ Write a definition, show an example, or draw a picture for each word or term in your list.

Math Vocabulary

Home Note: Your child creates a math vocabulary word list.

Glossary

common denominator

Fractions with the same denominator are said to have a common denominator.

$\frac{5}{8}$ and $\frac{7}{8}$ have a common denominator of 8.

common numerator

Fractions with the same numerator are said to have a common numerator.

$\frac{3}{4}$ and $\frac{3}{16}$ have a common numerator of 3.

denominator

The number below the fraction bar in a fraction is called the *denominator*. It tells how many equal parts are in the whole or how many objects are in a set. 4 is the *denominator* in $\frac{3}{4}$. In $\frac{3}{4}$, 4 indicates that the whole is divided into 4 equal parts or that there are 4 objects in the set. Both examples show 3 out of 4 in color.

Whole divided into 4 equal parts:

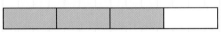

A set of 4 objects:

estimate (noun)

When you answer the question *About what will the answer be?* you make an *estimate*. Making an estimate in your head gives you an idea what the exact answer should be close to.

With adding and subtracting fractions, you can use this question to make an estimate: *Will the answer be about 1 whole, less than 1 whole, greater than 1 whole, or equal to 1 whole?* When we answer this question, we are making an estimate.

For example we can make an estimate for $\frac{2}{3} + \frac{5}{8}$ that the answer is greater than 1.

equivalent

Equivalent fractions are fractions that have the same or equal value. $\frac{2}{4}$ equals $\frac{1}{2}$ so, $\frac{2}{4}$ and $\frac{1}{2}$ are *equivalent fractions*.

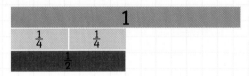

fraction

Fractions are numbers that name parts of a whole or parts of a set.

$\frac{5}{8}$ is a *fraction* that means 5 out of 8 equal parts.

They are written like this: $\frac{a}{b}$

$\frac{5}{8}$ of a whole

$\frac{5}{8}$ of a set

Glossary

fraction bar

A *fraction bar* is the line that separates the numerator and the denominator of a fraction.

In $\frac{3}{4}$, the red line is the fraction bar.

fraction equation

A *fraction equation* is a statement of equality between two expressions where one or both expressions contain a fraction. An example of a fraction equation is $\frac{1}{8} + \frac{7}{8} = 1$.

improper fraction

A fraction in which the numerator is greater than the denominator is called an *improper fraction*. It is always greater than 1. $\frac{5}{4}$ and $\frac{7}{5}$ are improper fractions.

lowest terms

A fraction is in *lowest terms* when the only number that can be divided evenly into both the numerator and denominator is 1. To rename a fraction in lowest terms means that you write it so that the only number that can be divided evenly into both the numerator and denominator is 1.

With fraction kit strips, *lowest terms* means building the fraction with the fewest strips. You can build trains with fraction strips equivalent to $\frac{1}{4}$ ($\frac{2}{8}$, $\frac{3}{12}$, $\frac{4}{16}$), but the $\frac{1}{4}$ strip uses the fewest pieces (1) so $\frac{1}{4}$ is in lowest terms.

$\frac{2}{4}$ is not in lowest terms. It can be renamed as $\frac{1}{2}$. $\frac{1}{2}$ is in lowest terms.

All unit fractions are in lowest terms. For example, $\frac{1}{8}$ is in lowest terms.

We also say that the fraction is in *simplest form*.

mixed number

A number is called a *mixed number* when part of it is a whole number and another part is a fraction. For example $1\frac{1}{4}$ is a *mixed number* because it has a whole number 1 and a fraction $\frac{1}{4}$. A mixed number can also be written as an improper fraction. $\frac{5}{4}$ is another way to write $1\frac{1}{4}$.

numerator

Numerator is the name for the number above the fraction bar in a fraction. 3 is the *numerator* in $\frac{3}{4}$.

It tells how many of the equal parts are being described. In $\frac{3}{4}$, the 3 tells you 3 parts out of a total of 4 equal parts.

3 of 4 equal parts are colored green. $\frac{3}{4}$ is green.

one-eighth or $\frac{1}{8}$

One-eighth is how you read $\frac{1}{8}$. It is a fraction and means one out of eight equal parts.

If you divide a whole into 8 equal parts, one of the parts is *one-eighth* of the whole.

If you divide a set of things into eight equal groups, each group is *one-eighth* of the whole.

one-fourth or $\frac{1}{4}$

One-fourth is how you read $\frac{1}{4}$. It is a fraction and means one out of four equal parts.

If you divide a whole into 4 equal parts, one of the parts is *one-fourth* of the whole.

 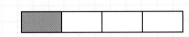

If you divide a set of things into four equal groups, each group is *one-fourth* of the whole set.

one-half or $\frac{1}{2}$

One-half is how you read $\frac{1}{2}$. It is a fraction and means one out of two equal parts.

If you divide a whole into 2 equal parts, one of the parts is *one-half* of the whole.

 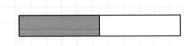

If you divide a set of things into two equal groups, each group is *one-half* of the whole set.

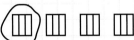

one-quarter or $\frac{1}{4}$

This is another way to say one-fourth.
(see one-fourth).

one-sixteenth or $\frac{1}{16}$

One-sixteenth is how you read $\frac{1}{16}$. It is a fraction and means one out of sixteen equal parts.

If you divide a whole into 16 equal parts, one of the parts is *one-sixteenth* of the whole.

 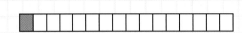

If you divide a set of things into sixteen equal groups, each group is *one-sixteenth* of the whole set.

one-sixth or $\frac{1}{6}$

One-sixth is how you read $\frac{1}{6}$. It is a fraction and means one out of six equal parts.

If you divide a whole into 6 equal parts, one of the parts is *one-sixth* of the whole.

 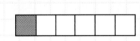

If you divide a set of things into six equal groups, each group is *one-sixth* of the whole set.

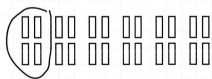

one-third or $\frac{1}{3}$

One-third is how you read $\frac{1}{3}$. It is a fraction and means one out of three equal parts.

If you divide a whole into 3 equal parts, one of the parts is *one-third* of the whole.

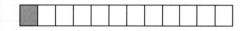

If you divide a set of things into three equal groups, each group is *one-third* of the whole set.

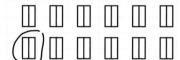

one-twelfth or $\frac{1}{12}$

One-twelfth is how you read $\frac{1}{12}$. It is a fraction and means one out of twelve equal parts.

If you divide a whole into 12 equal parts, one of the parts is *one-twelfth* of the whole.

If you divide a set of things into twelve equal groups, each group is *one-twelfth* of the whole set.

sequence

When numbers are arranged according to a pattern, the arrangement is called a *sequence*. In a *sequence* there is a comma between each number. A *sequence* ends with three dots to show it continues.

Here are two examples of sequences.

2, 4, 6, 8, 10, . . .

$\frac{1}{2}$, $\frac{2}{4}$, $\frac{3}{6}$, $\frac{4}{8}$, $\frac{5}{10}$, $\frac{6}{12}$, . . . This is called an *equivalent fraction sequence*.

simplest form

Another way of saying a fraction is in *lowest terms* is to say that it is in *simplest form*. (See lowest terms.)

unit fraction

A fraction in which the numerator is 1 is a *unit fraction*. It is one part of a whole. The whole can be divided into any number of equal parts. The fraction for one of those parts is a unit fraction.

For a whole divided into 4 equal parts, $\frac{1}{4}$ is one part and $\frac{1}{4}$ is a unit fraction.

whole

When you say $\frac{1}{4}$, you are talking about $\frac{1}{4}$ of a whole. It is important to know what the *whole* is because the whole determines the size of the fractional parts. For example, it is important to know the *whole* with pizzas because $\frac{1}{4}$ of a small pizza is less than $\frac{1}{4}$ of a large pizza. When you use your fraction strips, the *whole* is the dark blue strip and all of the other fraction strips are fractional parts of that *whole*.

Here are two wholes each divided into fractional parts. Each part is $\frac{1}{4}$.

 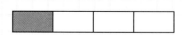

SCHOLASTIC

Do The Math™

Created by
Marilyn Burns

The Math on the Cover

Six pieces of chalk fit in each cubby. Look at the bottom 6 rows of cubbies. How many of those cubbies are completely filled? What is that fraction in lowest terms or simplest form?

SCHOLASTIC
www.scholastic.com

ISBN-13: 978-0-545-02270-5
ISBN-10: 0-545-02270-3

S0-AXD-517